Fantastically Festive CHRISTMAS Activity Book

ARCTURUS

ARCTURUS

This edition published in 2019 by Arcturus Publishing Limited
26/27 Bickels Yard, 151–153 Bermondsey Street,
London SE1 3HA

Copyright © Arcturus Holdings Limited

Cover illustrator: Morgan Huff
Book illustrations: Shutterstock
Author: JMS Books llp
Designer: Chris Bell, cbdesign

ISBN: 978-1-78950-734-8
CH007439NT
Supplier 29, Date 0719, Print run 8881

Printed in China

WELCOME TO A WINTER WONDERLAND OF PUZZLES!

We hope you enjoy the **Fantastically Festive Christmas Activity Book**. It's packed with drawing activities, fun puzzles, and games to keep you busy all season long. If you get stuck on any puzzles, the answers are on pages 86-96. Why don't you start by finishing this picture?

Shadow boxing

Take a look at this box crammed with toys. Can you work out which of the shadows below matches it exactly?

Stocking filler

Here's an easy way to draw a Christmas stocking. Just copy the picture square by square into the grid below.

Bauble bamboozle!

Study the order of the three baubles below. How many times can you find them in exactly the same order in the box? Search from left to right and from top to bottom.

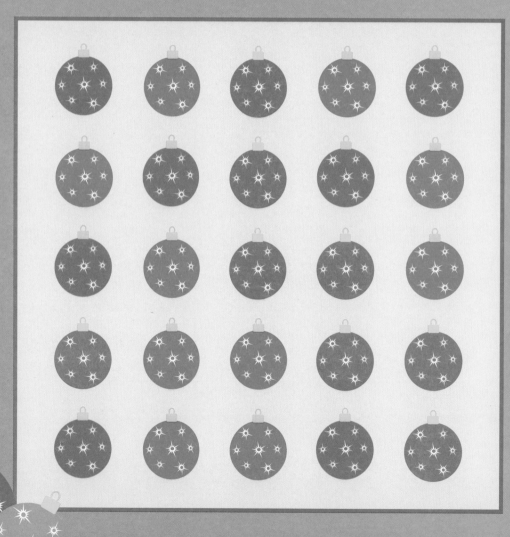

Frosty the Snowman

Learn how to draw Frosty in four easy steps.
Two circles are all you need to start.

1 First, draw two circles so they overlap, the bottom circle slightly bigger than the top.

2 Draw two half circles for his feet. Fill him in with white and add two twiggy arms. He needs some buttons for his coat.

3 Now draw his face. He has rosy cheeks, beady eyes, a carrot for his nose, and pebbles for his mouth.

4 Finish him off with a snazzy, stripy scarf. Make it bright, to stand out in the snow!

If you like, you can give Frosty a hat...

...a top hat,

...a warm knitted hat,

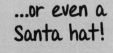

...or even a Santa hat!

Fairy dust

? 9 8 7 8 6 7 5

The Christmas fairy has been very busy sprinkling her fairy dust! Starting at the star nearest her wand, can you work out which number will complete the sequence?

The night before Christmas...

This little mouse has left some tasty cheese for Santa! Can you work out which stocking is his?

1. His stocking is mainly red.
2. His stocking contains a teddy bear.
3. His stocking has a red and green candy cane.
4. His stocking is not decorated with snowflakes.

Long-haul flight

a daanca

b daini

c cefnar

d oxcime

e weneds

Santa flies all around the world on Christmas Eve. Can you work out some of the countries he visits? The flags should help!

POLAR TREK

Finish this snowy scene of a polar bear.

On the wish list

I can't wait to play with it!

Join the dots to see what toy Santa has brought for Thomas. All aboard, please!

12

AWAY IN A MANGER...

There are six differences between these two nativity scenes. Can you find them all?

Cookie-doku!

Draw in the cookie shapes to complete the sudoku. Each row, column, and mini-grid should contain one of each item.

ME AND MY SHADOW

Can you find the
correct shadow for this
fun-loving snowman?

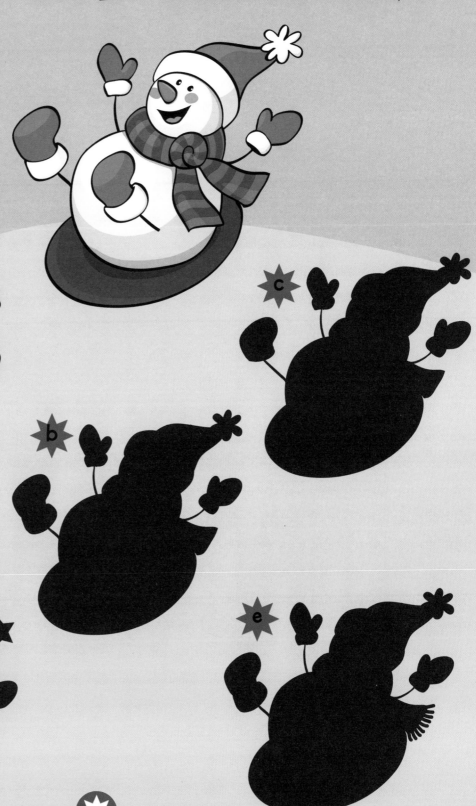

Little lost lamb

Can you help the shepherd find his lost lamb?

BY CANDLELIGHT

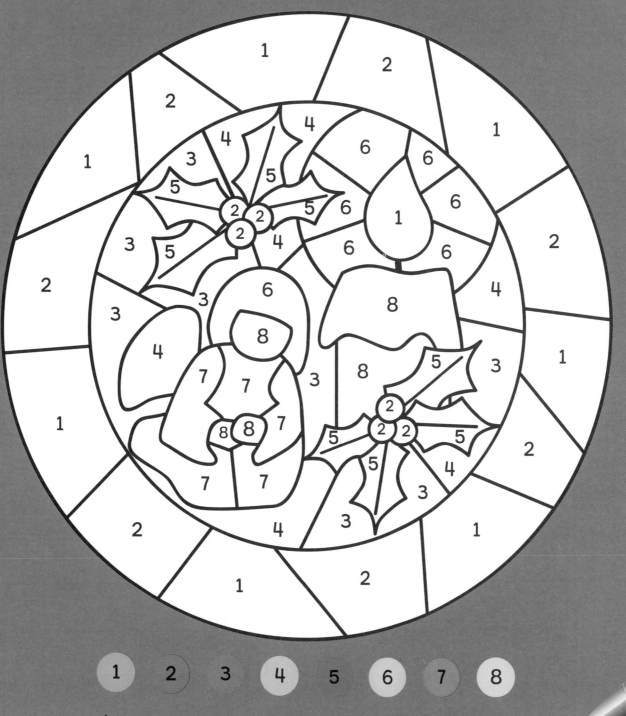

Paint this stained glass Christmas picture
using the numbers as a guide.

Twinkle, twinkle...

Starting at the arrow at the bottom and working upward, follow the numbers on the Christmas tree baubles. Can you work out which of the stars should go at the top?

36

35

38

START

18

BOXING CLEVER

Create your own designs on these parcels. Try spots, stripes, or stars!

SPOTS BEFORE YOUR EYES

Look at this dotty domino sequence. Which of the green dominoes completes the pattern?

a   b   c   d   e   f

Picture window

Look carefully at this picture, then turn over and answer
the questions on the next page. Try not to turn back!

Picture window questions

1. What is Santa holding in his left hand?

2. Is the ribbon on the wreath yellow or red?

3. What two toys can you see in Santa's sack?

4. How many parcels are sitting on the window ledge?

5. Is there a robin in the picture?

6. What shape is the window?

Try to avoid turning back for a quick peep!

22

Gridlocked

The mini-grid only appears once in the whole of the larger grid. Can you find it?

Where's Rudolph?

There's a whole herd of reindeer out for a walk
in the snow today! Can you spot Rudolph?

Winter warmers

Draw a circle around the odd one out
in each row.

ALL PRESENT AND CORRECT!

Which of these pretty presents appears in the box only once?

Sweet as candy

It's simple to draw this candy cane. Just draw the picture on the right into the grid below, copying it square by square.

Seasonal sequence

Which of the pictures below should replace the
question mark to finish the sequence correctly?

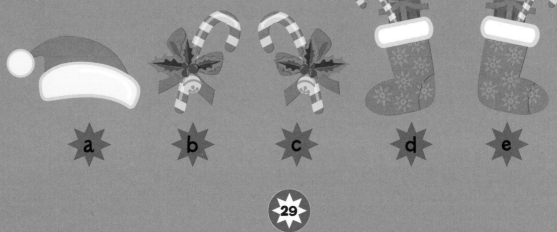

a   b   c   d   e

Present for a pooch

This cute puppy has got into a bit of a tangle.
Can you help him reach his present?

Pixie-in-boots

Evan the elf can't find his other boot.
Can you find it in the box above?
Draw a ring around the matching boot!

BOXING MATCH

When the figure on the right is folded to form a cube, just one of the four boxes below can be produced. Can you work out which one?

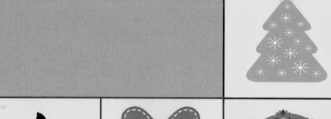

a

b

c

d

Study the pictures carefully!

TREE TEASER

How many trees can you see?

Winter mittens

Create your own
patterns on these
warm mittens.

Twit-twho?

These owls may all look the same, but each one differs in some small way from the others. Can you spot all the differences?

TREE-DOKU!

Draw in the trees to complete the sudoku. Each row, column, and mini-grid should contain one of each tree type.

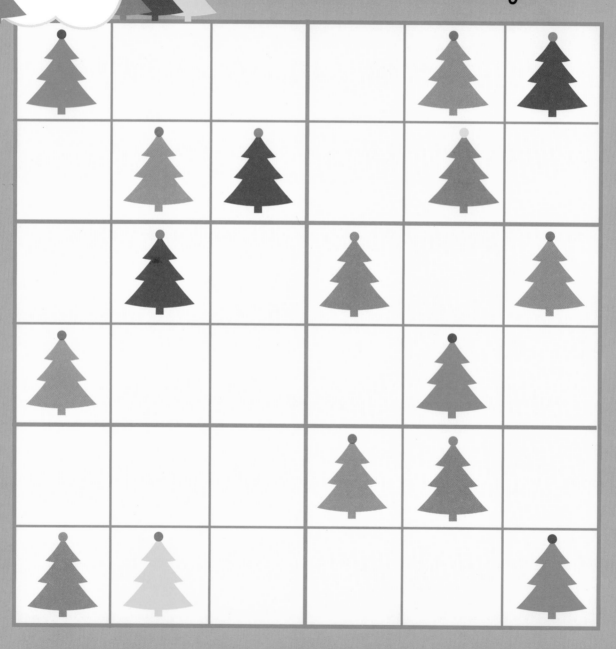

PERKY PENGUINS

Can you work out which of these penguins is different from the rest?

Top of the tree

Study this Christmas tree carefully. Can you work out which of the shadows below matches it exactly?

a

b

c

d

e

Rudolph, step-by-step!

Learn how to draw Rudolph in four easy steps!

1 Draw a circle for his head, then a rounded "L" shape for his body.

2 Give him two ears and two legs. He should be a rich shade of brown.

Give him a lighter stripe on his face.

3 Draw his antlers and two more legs; make them a darker shade. Add a little tail and a dark brown patch on his back.

4 Add his bright eyes and don't forget his red nose!

Add some cream spots on his back ...

... and a cream patch on his tail.

Missing piece...

a

b

c

d

Can you work out which of the segments on the right is the missing piece?
When you have found it, draw it into the larger picture.

PERFECT PETS

a carrot

b toy mouse

c bone

d saddle

e bird seed

These children have used their pocket money to buy presents for their pets. But which child has which pet? Draw a line between the child and their pet.

Pick a package...

Santa has sent Ella to pick up a package for him, but she can't remember which one. Can you help her find the box from the clues below?

1. The box has a pattern on it.
2. The box has a label.
3. The box does not have a red bow.
4. The box has a lid.
5. The box does not have stripes.

Can you help the frost fairy
reach her ice crystal?

FUN WITH FLAKES

How many snowflakes
can you count?

Snowtown

There are six differences between these two scenes of a snowy town. Can you find them all?

a

b

MAGIC NUMBERS

Work out the value of each object, so that the sums add up in each row and column, and write the numbers in the grid.

SHOCKING STOCKING!

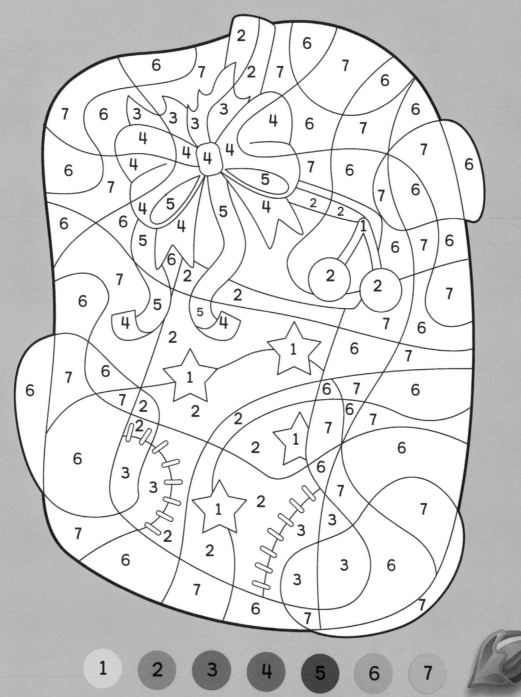

Finish this picture of a Christmas stocking,
using the numbers as a guide.

WREATHED IN MYSTERY

One of these wreaths has its baubles in a different order. Which one is it?

48

QUICK GETAWAY!

Look carefully at the picture, then turn the page and try to answer the questions.

QUICK GETAWAY QUESTIONS

1. Is the snowman's coat red or blue?

2. How many red berries did you see on the bush?

3. Is the snowman wearing a scarf?

4. What toy is in the snowman's sack?

5. What pattern is on the back of his mitten?

6. What creature is sitting on the bush?

7. Is it snowing?

When you have finished, turn back and check your answers!

DASHING THROUGH THE SNOW

Complete this picture of Rudolf. Use a red pen for his nose!

51

Christmas critters

Draw a circle around the odd one
out in each row.

ODD SOCKS

Which stocking does not have a matching pair?

TRICKY TRAIL

Can you find a route through these festive items? Follow them in this order all the way through. Use straight lines only, no diagonals!

start

1 2 3

finish

Make a wish...

He's so cute!

Join the dots to see which toy with a smiley face Santa has brought for Emily.

55

Gift tag teaser

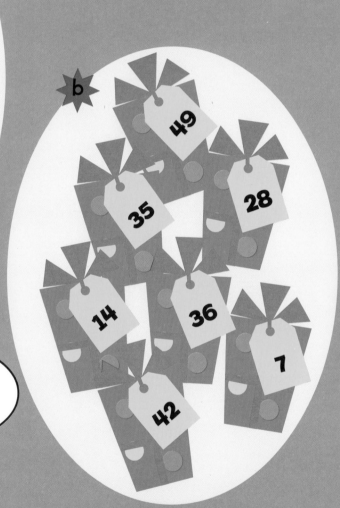

a

63
9
36
45
24
27
54

b

49
28
35
14
36
7
42

You'll need to know your times tables!

Can you work out which number is the odd one out in each group of gifts?

Domino theory

Each row of dominoes is one set. Look at the dots in each set.
Now look at the last line. Which of the red dominoes completes the sequence?

a   b   c   d

Cookie crumbs

Draw a circle around the odd one out
in each row.

Christmas kitty

Maisie wants to get to her Christmas present! Can you help her find it? Follow the strings carefully!

TAKE A BOW!

Use your brightest pens to complete these ribbons.

CHRISTMAS QUIZ

Can you answer the
questions below?

1. How many animals have four legs?

   _____

2. How many animals have feathers?

   _____

3. How many animals can you ride?

   _____

4. How many animals have horns?

   _____

Home from home

Use your paints or crayons to finish this happy holiday home.

Polar puzzle

There are six differences between these two snowy polar scenes. Can you find them all?

SLEIGH RIDE

Santa has noticed that each of these reindeer sleighs differs in some way from the others. Can you spot all the differences?

MIND THE DOTS

To see what's in the picture,
paint each individual section
in a shade to match its dot.

Shadow mouse

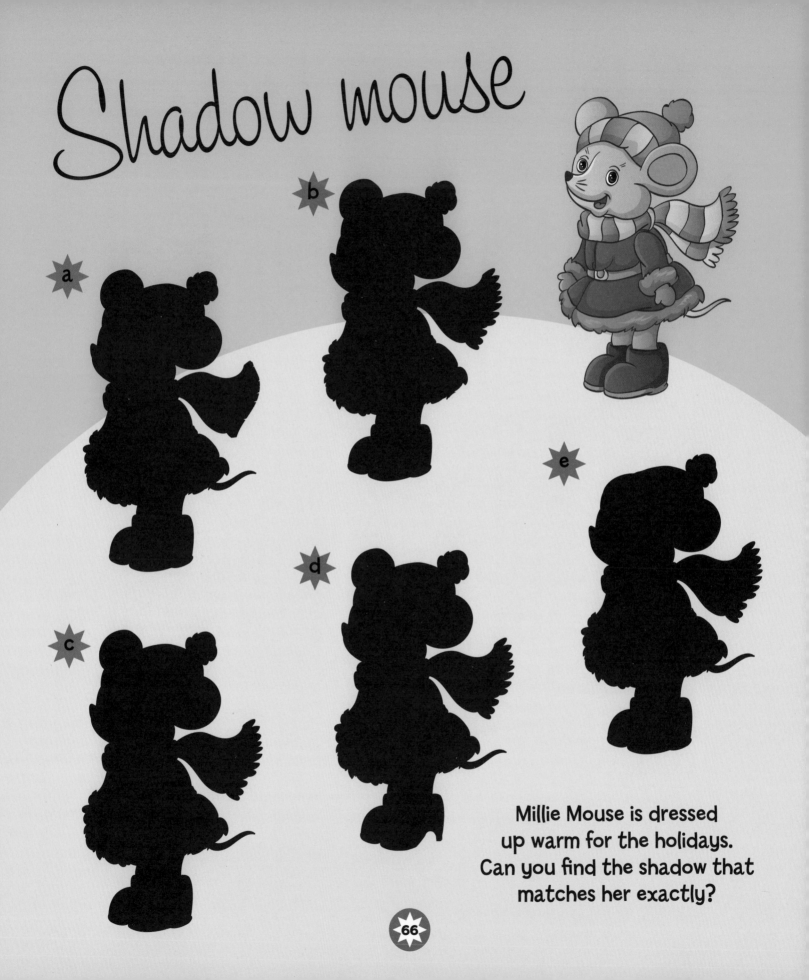

Millie Mouse is dressed up warm for the holidays. Can you find the shadow that matches her exactly?

Angelic twins

Which one of this angelic crew does not
have a matching pair?

BOW BELLES

How many bows
can you spot?

MOUNTAIN MAYHEM!

Which trail does Pedro need to take to reach his penguin pal?

FAST FAIRY!

To draw this pretty fairy, simply copy the picture in the grid square by square, then add some shading with pencils or pens.

IT'S IN THE BAG!

a enlap

b nunby

c tabo

d troob

e trocek

Sophie needs to put each of these toys in the correct bag above. Can you unscramble the letters and help her?

Playtime puzzle

Look carefully at the order of the three toys below.
How many times can you find them in exactly the same order
in the box? Search from left to right and top to bottom!

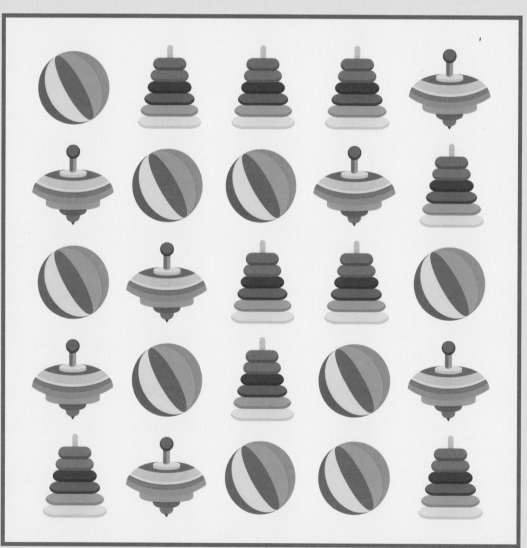

Stylish sweater

Design your own Christmas sweater. Try jazzy patterns or a festive picture!

Window on winter

Can you draw a wintry scene through the window?

SWEET SENSATIONS

Four of these sweet treats appear in the box more than twice. Can you spot which ones?

I love cookies!

Odd one out

Draw a circle around the odd one out in each row.

MUFFIN MAGIC

Joey wants a tasty muffin but they all look delicious!
Can you help him decide using the clues below?

1. He wants one with holly leaves.
2. He hates green frosting and blueberries.
3. He doesn't want a flower on his muffin.

Birdbrain teaser

a

b

c

d

Each of these bird pictures differs from the others in some small detail. Can you spot all the differences?

Little angel

Learn how to draw a helpful angel in four easy steps!

1 First, draw a circle for his head and a bell shape for his robe.

2 Give him tiny ears and arms. Shade in his head, neck, and hands, and use white for his robe.

3 Draw in his hair and collar and add his wings and feet. Fill in his wings and shoes a smart shade of lilac.

Give him a smiley face.

Draw in his halo.

Add some feathers on his wings.

4 Finish the angel's features. He's ready to do good deeds.

Baubles and bows

a

24

4

16

6

b

27

c

28

36

45

14

49

54

35

Each group of baubles shows
numbers from a multiplication table.
Can you work out which one?

SACK IT TO ME!

Look carefully at the picture, then turn the page and try to answer the questions.

SACK IT TO ME QUESTIONS

1. How many candy canes can you see in the sack?

2. Is there a snowman in the picture?

3. What pattern appears on the sack?

4. Is the teddy bear brown or white?

Use your memory, don't be tempted to take a quick peek!

5. Is the horse looking to the right or looking to the left?

Merry-doku

Draw in the faces to complete the sudoku. Each row, column, and mini-grid should contain one of each item.

TWIN TOYS

Which toy only appears once on the stocking?

PARTY OWLS

a b c d

The owls are having a Christmas party. Can you spot which of the owls on the branch is the odd one out?

ANSWERS

Page 4 SHADOW BOXING

Answer = **C**
In shadow A, the bobble on the puppet's hat is missing; in shadow B, the teddy has lost his ears; in shadow D, the ball next to the toy soldier is missing.

Page 6 BAUBLE BAMBOOZLE!

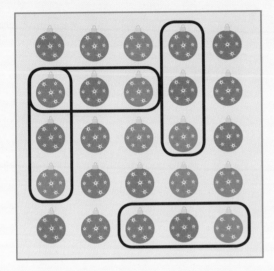

Page 8 FAIRY DUST

Answer = **10**
Moving upward through the sequence, add 2 for the next number, then subtract 1 for the next, and continue this sequence.

Page 9 THE NIGHT BEFORE CHRISTMAS...

Answer = **D**

Page 10 LONG-HAUL FLIGHT

Answers:
A = Canada; B = India; C = France;
D = Mexico; E = Sweden

Page 12 ON THE WISH LIST

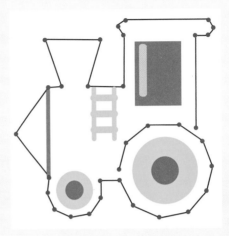

Page 13 AWAY IN A MANGER...

In picture B:
1. The shepherd has lost his crook.
2. The king on the left has lost his crown.
3. The rooster is missing a tail feather.
4. The king with the light brown hat has lost the feather in it.
5. The horse is missing its mane.
6. The gift brought by the king on the right has changed to blue.

Page 14 COOKIE-DOKU!

Page 15 ME AND MY SHADOW

Answer: **B**

In shadow A, the snowman has lost an arm; in shadow C, the snowman's boot has changed shape; in shadow D, the bobble on his hat has changed to a star; in shadow E, the snowman's scarf has a fringe.

Page 16 LITTLE LOST LAMB

Page 17 BY CANDLELIGHT

Page 18 TWINKLE TWINKLE...

Answer = **38**

Starting with the bottom bauble and moving upward, add 2, then 3, then 4, etc.

Page 20 SPOTS BEFORE YOUR EYES

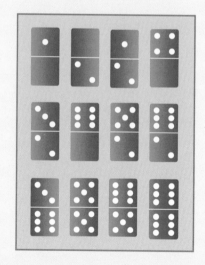

Answer = **A**

Start at the top left, and work in rows, from left to right, top to bottom. The spot total on each domino follows the sequence 1, 2, 3, 4, etc.

ANSWERS

Pages 21-22 PICTURE WINDOW

Answers:
1. A bell
2. Red
3. A doll and a teddy bear
4. Four
5. No
6. An arch

Page 23 ICE PALACE

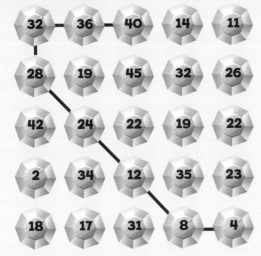

Page 24 GRIDLOCKED

Page 25 WHERE'S RUDOLPH?

Page 26 WINTER WARMERS

ANSWERS

Page 27   ALL PRESENT AND CORRECT!

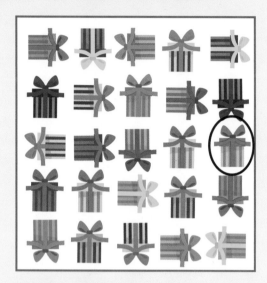

Page 29   SEASONAL SEQUENCE

Answer = **C**
The pattern is stocking, hat, candy cane, and the pictures alternate between facing right and facing left.

Page 30   PRESENT FOR A POOCH

Answer = **C**

Page 31   PIXIE-IN-BOOTS

Page 32   BOXING MATCH

Answer = **B**

Page 33   TREE TEASER

Answer = **9**

Page 35   TWIT-TWHO?

Page 36   TREE-DOKU!

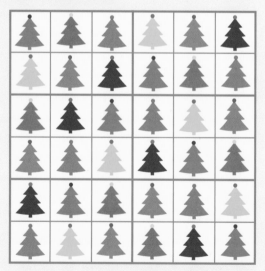

ANSWERS

Page 37   PERKY PENGUINS

Page 38   TOP OF THE TREE

Answer = **A**
In shadow B, two baubles on either side of the tree are missing; in shadow C, the right-hand parcel is missing; in shadow D, the plane is missing; in shadow E, the star has disappeared.

Page 40   MISSING PIECE...

Answer = **B**

Page 41   PERFECT PETS

Answers:
A = rabbit
B = pussy cat
C = puppy dog
D = horse
E = parrot

Page 42   PICK A PACKAGE

Answer = **D**

Page 43   FROSTY FOOTPATH

Page 44   FUN WITH FLAKES

Answer = **9**

Page 45 SNOWTOWN

In picture B:
1. The round window is missing from the building, far left.
2. The snowman has lost part of his scarf.
3. The Christmas tree is topped with a star.
4. The wreath on the street light has disappeared.
5. The front door has changed to blue on the building, far right.
6. The chimney pot is missing from the building, far right.

Page 46 MAGIC NUMBERS

3	7	3
4	2	4
7	3	2

 = 2

 = 7

 = 4

Page 47 SHOCKING STOCKING!

Page 48 WREATHED IN MYSTERY

Answer = **D**

Pages 49-50 QUICK GETAWAY!

Answers:
1. Red
2. Three
3. Yes
4. Toy rabbit
5. Snowflake
6. Robin
7. Yes

ANSWERS

Page 52 CHRISTMAS CRITTERS

Page 53 ODD SOCKS

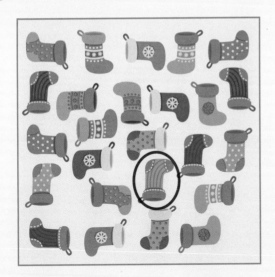

Page 54 TRICKY TRAIL

Page 55 MAKE A WISH...

Page 56 GIFT TAG TEASER

Answers:

A = **24**
All the other numbers can be divided by 9.

B = **36**
All the other numbers can be divided by 7.

Page 57 DOMINO THEORY

Answer = **C**
In each set, the dots on all four dominoes add up to 18.

Page 58 COOKIE CRUMBS

Page 59 CHRISTMAS KITTY

Answer = **C**

Page 61 CHRISTMAS QUIZ

1. Seven (goat, camel, cow, pig, sheep, horse, donkey)
2. Three (duck, hen, rooster)
3. Three (camel, horse, donkey)
4. Two (goat, cow)

Page 63 POLAR PUZZLE

In picture B:
1. A yellow bauble is missing from the tree.
2. A star has been added above the tree.
3. The wreath on the igloo is smaller.
4. There is an extra pile of snow in front of the igloo's door.
5. The smaller polar bear's scarf has changed from red to blue.
6. The big polar bear's ear is missing.

Page 64 SLEIGH RIDE

Answers:
A. The pattern on the sleigh has changed.
B. The top string of tree lights is missing.

ANSWERS

C. All the spots on the orange parcel have changed to blue.

D. Rudolph's bell has disappeared.

Page 65   MIND THE DOTS

Page 66   SHADOW MOUSE

Answer = **C**
In shadow A, the fringe of the scarf is missing; in shadow B, the mouse has lost her tail; in shadow D, she has heels on her boots; in shadow E, the mouse's right ear is missing.

Page 67   ANGELIC TWINS

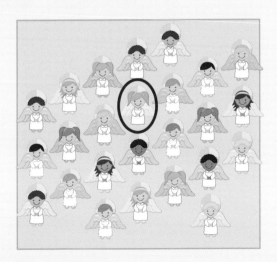

Page 68   BOW BELLES

Answer = **7**

Page 69   MOUNTAIN MAYHEM!

Answer = **C**

Page 71   IT'S IN THE BAG!

Answers:
A = plane; B = bunny; C = boat;
D = robot; E = rocket

Page 72   PLAYTIME PUZZLE

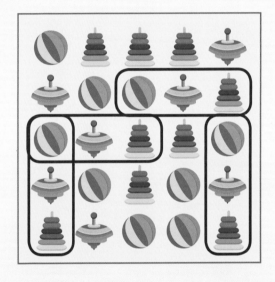

Page 75   SWEET SENSATIONS

Answers:
Mitten
Candy cane
Christmas tree
Long red bauble

Page 76 ODD ONE OUT

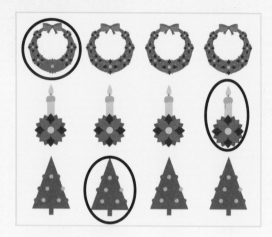

Page 77 MUFFIN MAGIC

Answer = **D**

Page 78 BIRDBRAIN TEASER

Answers:
A. The red patch on the bird's cheek is missing.
B. The bird's feet have changed from orange to yellow.
C. A bunch of berries is missing.
D. The bird has lost his tail.

Page 80 BAUBLES AND BOWS

Answers:
A = They are all multiples of 2
B = They are all multiples of 9
C = They are all multiples of 7

Pages 81-82 SACK IT TO ME!

Answers:
1. Four
2. No
3. Stars
4. Brown
5. To the left

Page 83 MERRY-DOKU

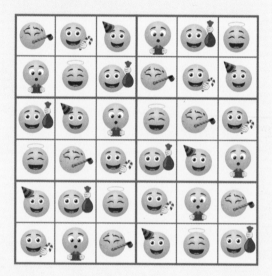

Page 84 TWIN TOYS

Answer:
Teddy bear

Page 85 PARTY OWLS

Answer = **C**
The orange and yellow stripes on the owl's hat are reversed.